Ladybird  Readers

Too Much Porridge!

Series Editor: Sorrel Pitts
Text adapted by Hazel Geatches
Activities written by Kamini Khanduri

LADYBIRD BOOKS

UK | USA | Canada | Ireland | Australia
India | New Zealand | South Africa

Ladybird Books is part of the Penguin Random House group of companies
whose addresses can be found at global.penguinrandomhouse.com.
www.penguin.co.uk www.puffin.co.uk www.ladybird.co.uk

Penguin
Random House
UK

First published 2020
001

Text copyright © Ladybird Books Ltd, 2020
All images copyright © Animaccord LTD, 2020

Masha and the Bear series created by: O. Kuzovkov
Masha and the Bear Art Director: I. Trusov

© Animaccord LTD, 2008 – 2020
www.mashabear.com

Printed in China

A CIP catalogue record for this book is available from the British Library

ISBN: 978–0–241–40187–3

All correspondence to:
Ladybird Books
Penguin Random House Children's
80 Strand, London WC2R 0RL

MIX
Paper from
responsible sources
FSC
www.fsc.org   FSC® C018179

Ladybird Readers

Too Much Porridge!

Based on the
Masha and the Bear TV series

Picture words

Masha

Bear

Hare

Wolves

Squirrel

Hedgehog

porridge

oats

jam

pot

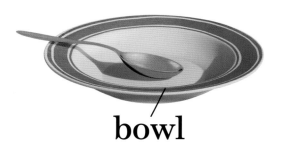

bowl

It was a nice, quiet day.
Bear was in his living room.

He wanted to play a game.

Then, Masha and Hare came to Bear's house.

"Bear, we're hungry," said Masha. "What can we eat?"

Bear was not happy. He wanted to play his game.

Bear quickly got a pot of porridge.

Then, he took his game and went outside.

Masha looked at the porridge.

"Yuck! I don't like Bear's old porridge," she said. "Let's cook some new porridge!"

11

First, she put some hot water in a very big pot.

Then, she put lots
AND LOTS of oats
in the pot.

Then, Masha added lots
AND LOTS of jam.

Then, she added lots
AND LOTS of milk.

Masha cooked the porridge.

Now, the porridge was pink from the jam!

"Oh, wow!" said Masha. "Mmm, pink porridge!"

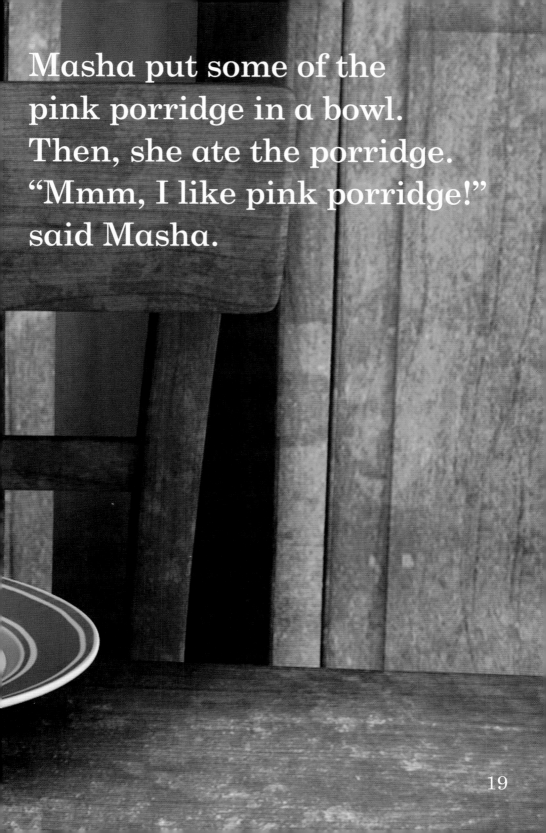

Masha put some of the
pink porridge in a bowl.
Then, she ate the porridge.
"Mmm, I like pink porridge!"
said Masha.

Then, Masha looked at the pot of porridge.

"Oh no!" she said.

There was too much porridge
in the pot!

Masha ran to the pot.
She put some porridge
in her bowl.

Then, Masha found every pot and bowl in the kitchen. She put the porridge in them.

Masha gave some porridge
to Hare. Now, he was
very fat!

Masha gave some porridge to Hedgehog, Squirrel, and the Wolves, too.

Now, they were all very fat!

Then, Bear came home.

Oh no! There was lots AND LOTS of pink porridge in the kitchen. Bear was angry. Masha had to clean Bear's kitchen.

Then, Bear's kitchen was clean again.

"Bear, I'm tired and hungry now. What can I eat?" Masha said.

There was lots AND LOTS of
pink porridge, of course!

Activities

The key below describes the skills practiced in each activity.

🖊 Spelling and writing

📖 Reading

💬 Speaking

❓ Critical thinking

✳ Preparation for the Cambridge Young Learners exams

1 **Match the words to the pictures.**

1 Masha   a

2 Hedgehog   b

3 Bear   c

4 Hare   d

5 Wolves   e

6 Squirrel   f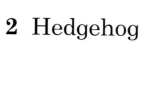

2 Circle the correct words.

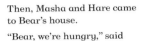

It was a nice, quiet day.
Bear was in his living room.

He wanted to play a game.

Then, Masha and Hare came
to Bear's house.

"Bear, we're hungry," said
Masha. "What can we eat?"

6

1 It was a nice, quiet

    a house.   **b** day.

2 Bear was in his

    a living room.   **b** dining room.

3 He wanted to play a

    a movie.   **b** game.

4 Masha and Hare came to Bear's

    a house.   **b** school.

3 Ask and answer the questions with a friend.

It was a nice, quiet day. Bear was in his living room.

He wanted to play a game.

Then, Masha and Hare came to Bear's house.

"Bear, we're hungry," said Masha. "What can we eat?"

Bear was not happy. He wanted to play his game.

Bear quickly got a pot of porridge.

Then, he took his game and went outside.

1 *What did Masha and Hare want?*

They wanted to eat.

2 What did Bear want to do?

He wanted . . .

3 What did Bear get?

He got . . .

4 **Circle the correct words.**

Masha looked at the porridge.

"Yuck! I don't like Bear's old porridge," she said. "Let's cook some new porridge!"

1 Masha **looked** / **smiled** at the porridge.

2 She said, **"Mmm!"** / **"Yuck!"**

3 Masha **liked** / **did not like** Bear's porridge.

4 She wanted to **cook** / **buy** some new porridge.

1 This is milk. ☒

2 These are oats. ☐

3 This is water. ☐

4 This is jam. ☐

5 This is a pot. ☐

6 **Circle the correct answers.**

1 What did Masha put in the pot first?

   a Hot milk.

   b Hot water.

2 How many oats did she put in?

   a Lots and lots of oats.

   b Not many oats.

3 Then, what did she add?

   a Lots and lots of honey.

   b Lots and lots of jam.

7 Look and read. Write *yes* or *no*.

Masha cooked the porridge.

Now, the porridge was pink from the jam!

"Oh, wow!" said Masha. "Mmm, pink porridge!"

16

17

1 Masha drank the porridge. ....no........

2 The porridge was yellow. ....

3 It was pink from the jam. ....

4 "Yuck, pink porridge!" said Masha. ....

8 **Look at the picture and read the questions. Write the answers.**

Masha put some of the pink porridge in a bowl. Then, she ate the porridge. "Mmm, I like pink porridge!" said Masha.

1 What color was the porridge?

It was .... pink ....

2 Where did Masha put the porridge?

She put it ....

3 Then, what did Masha do?

She ....

9 **Complete the sentences.**
Write a—d. 📖

1 Masha looked at ....c........

2 There was too much ....

3 Masha put some porridge ....

4 She found every pot and bowl ....

a in her bowl.

b in the kitchen.

c the pot of porridge.

d porridge in the pot!

10 Write the correct verbs.

Then, Masha looked at the pot of porridge. "Oh no!" she said.

There was too much porridge in the pot!

Masha ran to the pot. She put some porridge in her bowl.

Then, Masha found every pot and bowl in the kitchen. She put the porridge in them.

1 Masha **(look)** ....looked........ at the pot of porridge.

2 There **(be)** .... too much porridge in the pot!

3 Masha **(run)** .... to the pot.

4 Then, she **(find)** .... every pot and bowl in the kitchen.

5 She **(put)** .... the porridge in them.

40

11 **Find the words.**

bowl
porridge
pot
found
kitchen

n h o g b o w l w p v a k i t c h e n s k o y p o r r i d g e d l u f o u n d c b j e p o t m p f i

41

12 **Circle the correct pictures.**

1 This animal has big ears.

 a

 b

2 This animal lives in trees.

a

b

3 These animals are big and gray.

 a

b

13 **Read the text. Choose the correct words and write them next to 1—4.**

1 any	some	a lot
2 too	never	very
3 gave	giving	give
4 always	all	many

Masha gave [1] ____some____ porridge to

Hare. Now, he was [2] _____ fat.

Masha [3] _____ some porridge

to Hedgehog, Squirrel, and the Wolves,

too. Now, they were [4] _____ very

fat, too!

14 Write the missing letters.

er   el   ge   dg   ow

1  w a t e r

2  h e d _____ _____ h o g

3  b _____ _____ l

4  squirr _____ _____

5  porri _____ _____ e

15 **Look at the letters. Write the words.** 📖 ✏️ 🌼

| e m a c |

1 Then, Bear .... came .... home.

| d o p r i g e r |

2 There was lots AND LOTS of pink

....

| t h e n i c k |

3 The porridge was in the

....

| g r a n y |

4 Bear was ....

| a n c l e |

5 Masha had to ....
Bear's kitchen.

16 Talk about the two pictures with a friend. How are they different? Use the words in the box. 🗨

kitchen   cupboard   clean   floor   pink
window   wall   dirty   porridge

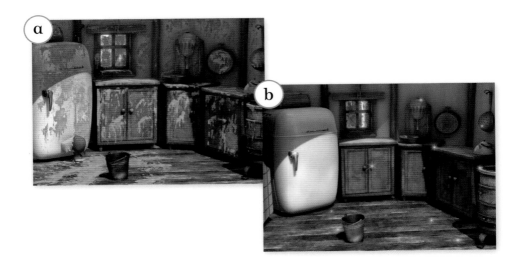

The kitchen is dirty in picture a. The kitchen is clean in picture b.

17 **Read the questions.**
Write the answers.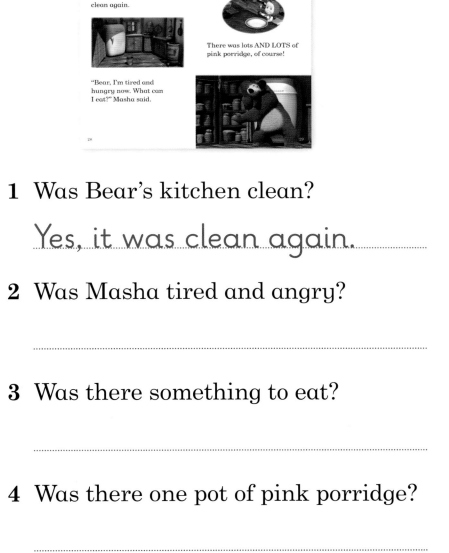

1 Was Bear's kitchen clean?

Yes, it was clean again.

2 Was Masha tired and angry?

....

3 Was there something to eat?

....

4 Was there one pot of pink porridge?

....

Ladybird Readers

✓ Digital edition of every title*

✓ Audio tracks (US/UK)

✓ Answer keys

✓ Lesson plans

✓ Role-plays

✓ Classroom display material

✓ Flashcards

✓ User guides

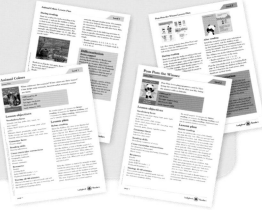